WORDS
WORDS
WORDS

With decorations by JUDY PIUSSI-CAMPBELL

WORDS WORDS WORDS

MARY O'NEILL

Doubleday & Company, Inc., Garden City, New York

Books by Mary O'Neill

HAILSTONES AND HALIBUT BONES
PEOPLE I'D LIKE TO KEEP
SAINTS: ADVENTURES IN COURAGE
WORDS WORDS WORDS

Library of Congress Catalog Card Number 66-10110

For Erin, Abigail and Johnny

FOR AN EARLY CHILD

Little one with honey on your lips
And berry stains on your chin,
I can see you standing
Barefooted in leopard skin
Staring at the morning.
Hair to your shoulders in a golden mat,
Wind-sniffing nose, darting, anxious eyes
In a world so new that even
The sun is a surprise.
Lightly on soles tough as leather
You make your curious way
Through great glooming forests
Into another day.
Stone in hand to fling at danger
You stop in a bluish, familiar place
And lean tip-toe over the still green water
To glimpse your face. . . .

And then you fade,
Dissolved in that long night
Before words lived—
Before man learned to write. . . .

MAN, ANIMALS AND WRITTEN WORDS

Elephants don't *wonder* about their trunks
Or try to *understand* the ways of skunks.
Lions don't tell stories or tear down
Jungle walls to *make* way for a town.
Tigers never *decorate* a house.
Leopards *show* no mercy for the mouse.
The fox in hunger pouncing on his prize
Learns nothing from a frightened rabbit's eyes.
None ever *plowed* a field or *planted* grain,
Or *bound* a wound or *healed* another's pain,
Or *broke* with stones the casing of the corn,
Or *sang* to heaven when a child was born.

Least of them all, far frailer than the fawn,
Early man was ill to look upon;
Hairy, with clawed hands and flung-down head
He groped for remnants after lions fed.
Prey of all things man slept in trees at first,
Hungered, frightened and consumed with thirst.
Keen to his scent, below him prowled the beast,
Awaiting dawn and the primeval feast.

Inside man's skull a torment no other creature knew,
A pendulum swinging and crying: "This is false! This is true!"
"You can think . . . and choose . . . and plan . . .
These are the magic qualities of MAN!
Lift up your head, for you alone can reason,
And master every problem in its season."

Man struck at first with clubs, and later stones,
And draped his neck with white, black-panther bones.
No other thing before had won a fight
By *using weapons* to increase its might.
Fear lessened, food increased, dream and desire
Broke cold and darkness: Man discovered fire!

How long between the hurled stone and the rose?
A million years? Nobody really knows.
From tools and drawings on old walls and rock
Man's history begins: a picture-clock.
The hands move slowly, driven by the mind
Toward abstract thoughts and, striking noon, they find
Reason's symbols sounding left and right—
The *alphabet of letters* is in sight!

This backward journey is the way we go
Through all recorded history that we know
To find our English is not old, but young—
And set with jewels from every other tongue!

NOBODY KNOWS WHAT THE FIRST WORDS WERE

Some people think
They were hisses and growls,
That sadness was snuffling
And anger was howls,
With happiness laughter
And punishment scowls—
A grit-graty language
Without any vowels!

Zst!

Grr.rr!

Zzzz-z!

Brr-rr!

ALPHABET

The signs that stand for sounds
Make up the alphabet
That's shaped a million words or more,
And isn't finished yet.

Most credit the Phoenicians
With developing this might
That gave us all the chance to read,
And better still . . . to write.

THE CONSONANTS AND VOWELS

Our vocal cords are harpstrings,
Our breath the hands that play
The music of our voices
In everything we say.
When breath *rubs* these strings together
The CONSONANTS will sound
Stiff-sharp and almost always
Hard as frozen ground. . . .
But when our breath just *whishes*
Past the harpstrings in our throats
The VOWELS begin to vibrate
And we hear the *liquid* notes. . . .

EGYPTIAN HIEROGLYPHIC WRITING

On tombs and walls
And jewels and cliffs
Egyptians carved their
Hieroglyphs.
A picture writing
Cut in stone,
In amber, ivory,
Bronze and bone.

If they chiseled
The wrong place
I wonder how
They could erase?

ENGLISH BEGINS

The English language
Opens its door
With four Celtic words:
Bin, dun, crag and *tor*:
Bin for firewood,
Grains and roots,
Basket, manger,
Box for boots.
Crag for hard
Upthrusting stones
That tore men's muscles
And men's bones.
Dun for thunder,
Smashing seas;
Sounds of terror
And unease.
Tor for mountains
Green and high
Scratching history
On the sky.

WHAT IS THE ENGLISH LANGUAGE?

English is a way of speech
Whose early, old beginnings reach
Into the drifting mystery
Of time ahead of history.
But, as our knowledge grows,
There's good reason to suppose:

The mother of English is Aryan.
Lands 'round the Caspian Sea
Shaped its form and cadence,
And its first melody.
There's Celtic in it,
And a Germanic ring
Iron and hard as the spiked crown
Of a Teutonic king.

The bones of English are Greek.
The muscle of English is Latin.
The flesh of English is as French
As lustrous silk or satin.
The eyes of English are blue
Though often the dark hue
Of Egypt, Spain, and Syria
Shine in them too.

And in the blood of English
The Arab and the Turk
Mix with the Norman peasant
And the Babylonian clerk.
Norsemen and Phoenician
Extend its power and length;
Rome gives English sinew
And its simple strength.
English ears are Druid;
In their wrinkled shells
A sea-sound plays in lovely
Murmurings and swells.
Its brow's a freckled road map
Of Finland, Ireland, Wales;
Most English words are fluted
With the singing of the Gaels.
And from its throat comes rippling
Along a Sanskrit jaw
The thundrous, mighty words in which
English states the Law.
English drinks of China tea
And wears bright Asian silk,
And English goes quite Scottish
Over oaten cakes and milk.
This language borrows freely
Fresh marrow for its bone;
From every tongue upon the earth
It takes something for its own.

THE WRITTEN WORD

Words are the bridges we build
To reach each other.

Hands can talk. By touch they say
Many things in a clear, distinct way.
They can wave, hold, shake, pat and point,
Soothe, slap, curl, give, take and anoint.
Eyes can talk. By look they tell
Many a thing that mouths hide well.
But to bring an idea from back of a face
Shaped to perfection and spun into space,
And held up to feast the whole human race
Alive in performance, still supple and true
This—only the written word can do!

SYLLABLE

Words are made of one or many sounds.
Each sound is called a syllable—
There's one in *fill,* two in *fulfill*
And five in *unfulfillable.*

A SENTENCE

A sentence is a group of words
Expressing a complete thought.
It needs a subject and a predicate:
The kidnaper was caught.

A declarative sentence expresses a fact:
The diplomat behaves with tact.

An interrogative sentence wants to know:
Who is that? Is it going to snow?

An imperative sentence commands or forbids:
Listen to me. Stop blinking your lids.

An exclamatory sentence exclaims in wonder:
Oh, what a day! BOOM goes the thunder!

20

PHRASE

A phrase brings to a sentence
A single little notion
That has no finite verb to give it
Independent motion:
If I were you I would not go
Out to play in the wet snow.

INTERJECTION

An interjection is an exclamation
Independent of grammatical relation,
Expressing strong feeling or claiming attention:
Horrors! It was too horrible to mention!
Darling! What a beautiful dress!
Jeepers! Isn't this room a mess?

PARAGRAPH

A paragraph is a short composition
In which every sentence unites
To clarify a particular point
About which the author writes.

VERBS

To words a verb's
The main attraction—
Because it puts them
Into action.

NOUN

A noun is the name of a person,
Plant, idea, thing or place,
As *boy, girl, city, town,*
Horse, bird, rose or *face.*

PREPOSITION

Often a word under certain conditions
Becomes the object of prepositions:
They are fond *of* blue. I am fond *of* you.
Then nouns and pronouns change their ways
To become an adverbial or adjectival phrase:
The man *with* the red face ran the best race.
That little mouse came from *outside* the house.

PRONOUNS

You're using a pronoun
When you refer
To anyone as:
Him, His or Her,
A Who or a Whom,
Or a He or a She,
A They or a Them,
A You or a Me.
But the one you'll use most
Is a two-letter bit—
The popular, marvelous,
Lazybone: IT!

CONJUNCTIONS

A conjunction's the word
Between sister *AND* brother
That keeps them from running
Smack into each other.

A conjunction's a word
That adds to a thought:
"*BUT* I don't always do
The things that I ought!"

A conjunction's a word
That expresses a choice:
"I can whisper *OR* scream
With my only-one voice!"

25

ADJECTIVES

Adjectives tell you the quality of a person, place or thing
As, *pretty* girl, *big* city, *fast* horse, *golden* ring.
Some adjectives increase their strength
By going on to greater length:
As, *"pretty"* when you're *positive* she's fair,
But *"prettier"* whenever you *compare,*
And see a second more exquisite face
Among the members of the human race.
But, *"prettiest"* is where you reach the top—
Superlative—and there you have to stop.

ANTONYMS—SYNONYMS—HOMONYMS

Antonyms, synonyms, homonyms
Are not as difficult as they sound,
And they do give a wonderful choice
Of words to pass around:

Antonyms oppose each other:
Good and bad—sister and brother.

Synonyms mean *almost* the same:
Glad and joyful—amusement, game.

Homonyms agree in sound
As *knew* and *gnu,*
But differ as widely in meaning
As *too* and *two.*

PERIOD

When you come to the end of a written thought
You just sign-off with a polka dot.

COMMA

A sentence is a band of words
Going for a walk.
A comma is a pause for breath
Taken as you talk.
And when you write, a comma is
Set down just because
It's time you gave your reader a
Little chance to pause.

EXCLAMATION POINT

At the end of a word or a line to excite,
Scare or command it is proper to write

QUESTION MARK

Symbol of all I wish I knew
Polka dot under a curlicue. . . .

APOSTROPHE

Apostrophes are floating commas that show who owns a thing,
As in *mama's* shoe, *boy's* hat, *man's* glove, *girl's* ring.
Apostrophes can shrink words as do not into *don't,*
Have not into *haven't* and will not into *won't.*

SEMI-COLON

More than a comma, not quite a full stop;
A semi-colon is a sentence prop
Used to hold back an independent clause,
And clarify its meaning with a necessary pause.

The room is filled with chairs; they are arranged in pairs,
designed to be admired, and a comfort to the tired.

COLON

A colon gives a sentence a chance
To call a halt and then advance.

QUOTATION MARKS

Quotation marks are the curls that enclose
What someone else said in verse or in prose—
Exactly that—nothing less or more—
That's one thing quotation marks are for:
The boy with the bright green bicycle said:
"Oh, how I wish it were bright red!"

The first speaker's words lie inside this sign

When quoting another he halves the design:

My mother said: "The other day
I heard our next-door neighbor say:
'I love these short, light summer rains
Because they wash our windowpanes.' "

DASH

Dash is a sign that writers make
Whenever their thoughts switch or break.

HYPHEN

A hyphen is a small straight line that joins two words together
As, rag-tag, tip-top, tree-toad and fair-weather.

A hyphen at the end of a line of written text
Tells you that the last word is completed on the next.

PARENTHESES

Parentheses are the clamps that grip
An aside, an afterthought or quip
That a sentence could often do without—
But you simply have to tell about.

I saw a boy (and his name is Harry),
Planting tulips in January.

FEELINGS ABOUT WORDS

Some words clink
As ice in drink.
Some move with grace
A dance, a lace.
Some sound thin:
Wail, scream and pin.
Some words are squat:
A mug, a pot,
And some are plump,
Fat, round and dump.
Some words are light:
Drift, lift and bright.
A few are small:
A, is and all.
And some are thick,
Glue, paste and brick.
Some words are sad:
"I never had. . . ."
And others gay:
Joy, spin and play.
Some words are sick:
Stab, scratch and nick.
Some words are hot:
Fire, flame and shot.
Some words are sharp,
Sword, point and carp.

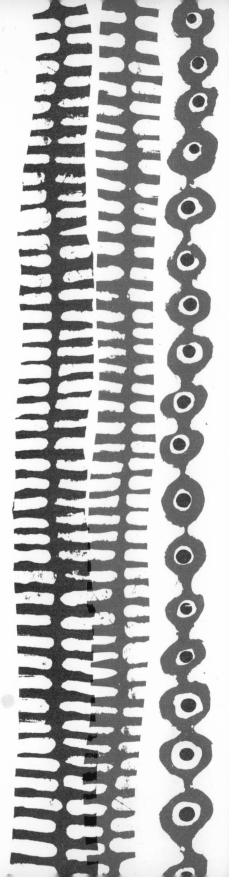

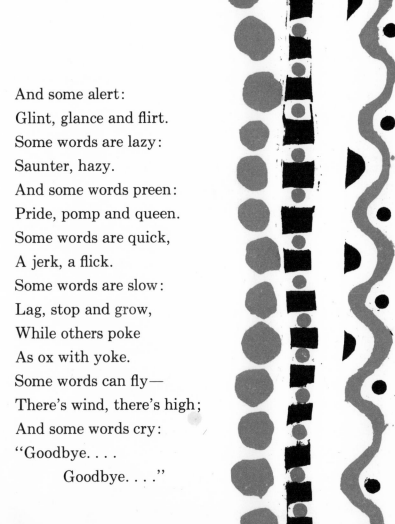

And some alert:
Glint, glance and flirt.
Some words are lazy:
Saunter, hazy.
And some words preen:
Pride, pomp and queen.
Some words are quick,
A jerk, a flick.
Some words are slow:
Lag, stop and grow,
While others poke
As ox with yoke.
Some words can fly—
There's wind, there's high;
And some words cry:
"Goodbye. . . .
          Goodbye. . . ."

IMAGINATION

Imagination is a new idea beginning to grow
In the warm, soft earth of all we know.

THOUGHTS

Thoughts are ideas,
And sometimes they're notions,
Springing from senses and emotions.
Deep in the darkness of the mind
Thought makes decisions, helps us find
Our way through all it means to live,
To learn, to love, create, forgive.
In this we humans are distinct:
The only creatures who can think.

ETCHINGS

Sunshine shapes on bedroom ceilings,
Curling-down potato peelings,
Army jets as small as flies
Crawling across summer skies,
Junkyard humps red-rimmed with rust,
Bird-claw patterns in the dust,
Shadows stretching on a wall,
Twigs, as your eye sees them fall,
Leafless trees as stiff as kings,
And all such silent-speaking things. . . .

RECOLLECTION

A brain isn't much larger
Than a good-size coffee cup,
But no one in a lifetime
Has ever filled one up.
Everything you taste or touch,
Smell or hear or say,
Feel or think or fashion
Finds a place to stay.
And quickly to your bidding,
Behind the shutters of your eyes
Flash back your impressions
Full-color and life-size:
Circus clown,
Water flow,
Down town,
Christmas snow,
Lady in brown
You never knew
Who turned one day
And smiled at you.
Shape of cross,
Rough of stone,

Plush of moss,
Round of bone,
Stretch of sea,
Soft of bed,
Apple tree and
Curly head,
Noise of cheers,
Taste of meat,
Smart of tears,
Running feet,
Smell of peach,
Form of face,
Bluff and beach,
Every thing, every place. . . .

MEMORY

Memory is a tape recorder
And there's one in every head
Storing everything we've ever seen,
Or felt, or heard, or said.
The word, *remember,* simply means
We're playing back a part
Of all that's been recorded there
And lives close to our heart.
Sad thing, sweet thing,
Whatever it be,
The calling it back is a
Memory.

HOPE

Hope is a climber,
A brimming cup,
The elevator that only
Goes up,
A chair lift,
Over the drop
Swinging you to the
Mountaintop—
Sunlight at a
Tunnel's end,
Broken spirit
On the mend.
Hope is the stretch
You make to reach
The branch that holds
The perfect peach.
Hope is a bird
Learning to fly,
Wobbling after
Many a try
Then taking off
To the giddy high,
Windy blue silk
Summer sky.

Hope is the strain
Beyond your strength
That adds an inch
To your inward length.
Hope is the moment
When you jump
Up from the tumble,
Out of the slump.
Hope is the light in the awful dark,
The clear, bright-blazing, beckoning spark
That sets your feet to a running pace
For one little look at her beautiful face.

FORGET

Forget is a hider
In a long black cape,
A thing that has happened
And wants to escape
Back to the place where
Nothingness lies,
Long before sadness
Or surprise.
But the brain's too clever,
And it says to Forget:
"Hide if you want to
But I'll use you yet!"
Hide that you bumped
Someone in the park.
Hide that you're still
Afraid of the dark.
Hide that you pinched
Your little brother,
And stole a penny
From your mother.
Hide even the word
You still can't spell
Because you didn't learn it
Very well.

Forget is a digger,
Its trenches are deep
And there disappointments
Curl up and sleep.
New grass velvets
The raw-earth scar,
Until only Forget knows
Where they are.
Then comes a Springtime,
Or maybe a Fall,
When you can't quite remember
They happened at all.
Days can go by,
And weeks and years,
Before your hand touches
Or your ear hears
Or your eyes see
Something that wakens
A memory.
Then what you forgot
Jumps up to say:
"You saw me, or felt me
Or heard me one day.
Nothing that happens
Goes truly away. . . ."

PRECISION

Precision is a multiplication table
And a railroad track,
A clock's tick,
A duck's quack,
Rick-rack braid's
Even points,
The engineering
In our joints.
The length of time
From here to there,
The size of everything
We wear,
The cup of sugar
In a cake,
The rate of shudder
In a quake.
Precision loathes
Suppose and Guess.
Its only words are:
"No!" and "Yes!"
Its only love
Is old Exact.
Its only food, of course,
Is Fact. . . .

QUESTION

If I can be bedeviled
Can I be be-angeled, too?
Was anyone disgusted
Ever gusted that you knew?
Was distinguished ever tinguished,
And tell me, is it true,
Distorted things are torted
In another point of view?

EPITHET

An Epithet is an insult
Rolled in poison spittle,
Said to make a person feel
Mean and wrong and little.
An Epithet is a dagger
Of words that know the way
To strike, sting, twist, turn,
Dig inside and stay. . . .

SMILE

A smile is pleasure as it slips
Out to do push-ups on your lips.

LAZY

Lazy is a word
That makes you think
Of gluggy grease
In a stopped-up sink—
Of minds that float
In rivers of fat
Bungling into
This and that.
Slow to start
And last to finish
All lazy does
Is to diminish.

FROWN

Frown: a puckering of forehead skin
To show off your displeasure in.

GOSSAMER

Gossamer is a thin and lovely thing
Almost not there. . . .
It's dandelion down
On the summer air,
Sun sliding over
Long, spread-out hair,
A spider's spin
Across the meadow grass
Where dew beads roll
As glittering as glass—
A sudden thought
That scampers through the mind
And hides, and later is
Impossible to find.
Lace in the hand,
And a falling feather,
Twilight time in
Misty weather,
River fog,
Milkweed fluff,
Cloud drift,
Smoke puff,
Wild fern and
Dreams that rise
In that dark blue place
Behind your eyes. . .

"K" IS A BOOB

If I were a "K"
I'd never agree
To open the spelling
Of *knew* and of *knee*.
If a *person* did that
He'd be led by the wrist
To the door of the nearest
Psychiatrist. . . .

"G" HAD A CRICKET IN ITS DOME

"G" had a cricket in its dome
The day it attached itself to *gnome*. . . .

Someone had very little to do
The day they put "g" in *gnat* and *gnu*.

WHAT IS THE MATTER WITH "P"?

"P" is really
Quite erratic
When it heads
The word *pneumatic,*
And sadder than
A dead begonia
As it leads off
In *pneumonia,*
And it should have
An anaesthetic
To amputate it
From *phonetic* . . .
And can anyone
Explain to me
Why *ptarmigan*
Begins with "P"?

MEAN

Mean is to twist
Somebody's ear
When an older person
Isn't near.
Mean is to lie,
And annoy,
Ruin a rapture
Or a toy.
Mean is to diminish
With ridicule and taunt
Those things of others
That you want.
Mean is a coward's
Favorite game,
In which the winner
Shifts the blame.

Mean are words
That carry sting
In their meaning,
In their swing.

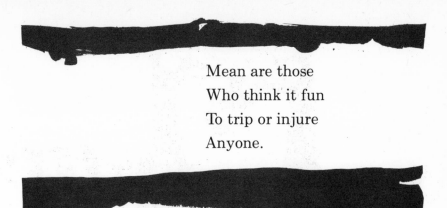

Mean are those
Who think it fun
To trip or injure
Anyone.

Mean is a cold and
Narrow heart
In which the cruelest
Rumors start.
Poverty is a Mean
You can see
And it scrimps those who have it
Terribly.
Mean is a kiss
From a traitor's lips
As fakey as
False fingertips.
Mean is a stingy,
A greedy, a curt,
Its only purpose
Is to hurt.
Mean is a difficult
Thing to erase
Once it's written
On a face. . . .

GOOSEBERRY

When English was young
Did the wild geese cry
For gooseberry cobbler
And gooseberry pie?
When English was young
Did the mother goose hatch
Her soft golden gaggle
In a gooseberry patch?
You don't think that's it?
Then why are the names
Of such different things
So exactly the same?

And how is this berry—
All skin, seed and juice—
Like the web-footed waddle
And honk of a goose?
Could it be that the down
That a gooseberry wears
Was clipped before cooking
And sold at the fairs?
And used as a stuffing
By many an oldster
To fatten a mattress
Or feather a bolster?
This could be the answer,
For however abstruse—
It's the only thing common
To berry and goose.

GROVEL

Shovel and grovel are rather alike
And they both are related to ground
One is to dig with—the other one means
Your character's crawling around.

PATIENCE OR CONCOMDURE?

Boy and girl,
Sire and dame,
Help me find Patience
A better name.
For Patience sounds
Like a lady in brown
Ironing pleats in her forehead
To further her frown.
But it means to be *con*stant,
*Com*posed, to en*dure*. . . .

52

Then shouldn't it sound
A bit more like *secure?*
So, if from constant
We snip off the *con,*
As a beginning,
And if we go on,
Take *com* from composed
(And it won't mind a bit),
We're getting an inch or two
Closer to it.
We now have *concom,*
And so from endure
We'll clip the last syllable
Just to be sure.
CONCOMDURE! It's perfect!
Why, *I* could be that—
Concomdurely sitting
And stroking my cat.
You don't like *concomdure?*
You like *patience* more?
Then I guess I'll slip quietly
Out the back door. . . .

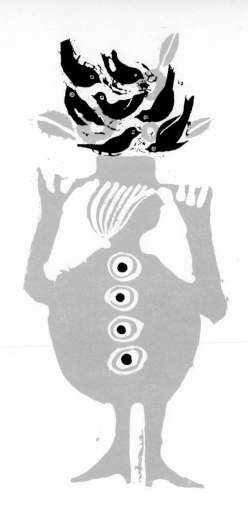

HAPPINESS HAS FIVE CHILDREN

CONTENT is the one whose touch you feel
After you've had a wonderful meal,
Or when you waken without a call
Rested and without any worry at all.
CONTENT is pillowy, round and fat
With seven sparrows in her hat.

GLAD glides in when you could use
A little present of good news.
She's the one who lights your eyes
With little sparkles of surprise.
She's rather plump and not too tall
And pink is her favorite color of all.

GAY'S visits are short. She arrives in a flurry
Of laughter and thrills and she leaves in a hurry.
She's terribly young and amazingly smart
At loosening the latchets that fasten your heart.
She's stemmy-thin and bon-bon sweet
And hummingbirds fly her down the street.

JOY lifts your spirit up so high
It can touch the blue-soft of the sky.
It can hear the top wind's silvery singing
And the tinkly bells of rapture ringing.
JOY'S terribly shy. Her visits are rare
And she wears moonbeams in her hair.

DELIGHT comes quiet as a mouse
Into the rooms of your heart's house.
She lights the lamps and makes the glow
Of the sweetest smiles you'll ever know.
She'll have wild-honey on her lips
And candle flames for fingertips. . . .

It's hard to believe,
All these are less
Than one quick touch
Of HAPPINESS. . . .

FASCINATION

Fascination is worth a mention
The way it gobbles up attention.
To have it you
Must captivate,
Bewitch, enrapture,
And elate.
Hold with spells
And charm and wile.
To fascinate is to
Beguile.
It's beautiful
To its beholder
Whether young or
Whether older.

Fascination's
Full of wit,
Nothing can
Compare with it.
Always present,
Never late,
Or tired, or faintly
Out of date.

Full of grace
As flowing milk,
Soft of voice
As China silk.

Fascination
Stands you still
And makes a ribbon
Of your will.
It can be real
It can be fake—
Warm your heart
Or see it break.
It can be part
Of place or play,
Man or woman,
Night or day
Art or science,
Or a book,
And sometimes it is
Just a look.

SLOPPY

Sloppy means: Nothing
Where your hand can find it.
And Sloppi*ness*:
Is not to mind it.

Run-down shoes,
Tipped-over trash,
Half-done lessons,
Untied sash,
Dirty neck and
Undone dishes,
Living on a lot
Of wishes.
Window curtain
Torn and flapping,
Little work and
Too much napping,
Dresser drawers
An awful mess,
Dribbles on a
Party dress—
What Sloppy leads to
You can guess. . . .

FELICITY

Felicity is a word
Meaning pleasure and grace
As they come from a person,
A thing or a place.
Felicity has an
Elegant air,
As the perfect shape
Of a little chair,
Or a girl with sapphires
In her hair.
When Felicity speaks
The sounds you hear
Lie like velvet
On your ear—
Every word so
Apt and choice
Arranged in an exquisite
Tone of voice.
And through it all
Adding warmth to style
Runs the ribbon
Of a smile. . . .

BALM

Balm is a lotion
Soft as rain.
Balm is a soother
Against pain.
Balm is so healing
It's hard to tell
Where the hurt was
When you're well.

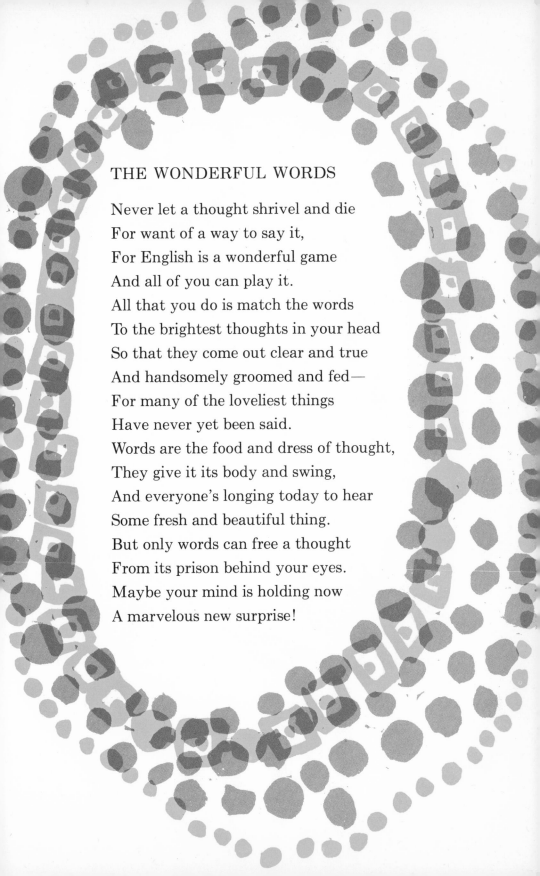

THE WONDERFUL WORDS

Never let a thought shrivel and die
For want of a way to say it,
For English is a wonderful game
And all of you can play it.
All that you do is match the words
To the brightest thoughts in your head
So that they come out clear and true
And handsomely groomed and fed—
For many of the loveliest things
Have never yet been said.
Words are the food and dress of thought,
They give it its body and swing,
And everyone's longing today to hear
Some fresh and beautiful thing.
But only words can free a thought
From its prison behind your eyes.
Maybe your mind is holding now
A marvelous new surprise!

MARY O'NEILL was raised in what she describes as a wonderful barn of a Victorian house in Berea, Ohio, where she wrote and directed plays for her younger brothers and sisters. She was educated at Our Lady of Lourdes Academy, Saint Joseph's Academy, and Western Reserve in Cleveland and the University of Michigan. Mrs. O'Neill entered the advertising field and became a partner in her own advertising agency. She has retired from advertising and now lives in New York City. This book is her fifth book for young readers.

Mrs. O'Neill's previous books include the very popular books of verse, HAILSTONES AND HALIBUT BONES and PEOPLE I'D LIKE TO KEEP, and the distinguished SAINTS: ADVENTURES IN COURAGE.

Artist JUDY PIUSSI-CAMPBELL was born in South Bend, Indiana. She was graduated from De Pauw University, and did post-graduate work at L'Académie de la Grande Chaumière in Paris. She returned to this country for five years, but since 1962 has been a resident of Florence, Italy, where her husband teaches at the University of Florence. They have two children.

In addition to illustrating books for both children and adults, Mrs. Piussi-Campbell creates textile and graphic designs. She is a "reluctant mountain climber and a bad skier" and a very adventurous cook.